One hundred more or less

Write the number which is 100 more than:

1. 372
2. 589
3. 294
4. 804
5. 216
6. 899

Write the number which is 100 less than:

7. 438
8. 207
9. 143
10. 911
11. 230
12. 601

Large and small

1. Which is more, 312 or 321?
2. Which is lighter, 6·5 kg or 6 kg?
3. Which is less, £3·99 or £3·09?
4. Which is shorter, 67 cm or 1 m?
5. Which is heavier, 898 g or 989 g?
6. Which is more, £0·10 or £10·00?

Put these in order, the largest first.

7. 321, 123, 312, 231, 132
8. £1·99, £9·91, £9·19, £9·99, £1·90
9. 6·50 m, 5·50 m, 5·20 m, 7·20 m, 6·20 m
10. 703, 307, 730, 370, 377
11. 587 g, 498 g, 678 g, 598 g, 489 g
12. 325p, £4·65, 395p, £4·25, £3·85

In between

< means *less than*;
> means *greater than*.

HELP BOX

Write a number which would make the number sentence correct.

1. 12 < ☐ < 15
2. 195 < ☐ > 205
3. Write all the odd numbers between 80 and 90.
4. Write all the even numbers between 297 and 310.

Write the number which is halfway between:

5. 60 and 70
6. 180 and 220

Write an amount which is between:

7. 15 kg and 16 kg
8. £8 and £9
9. What whole numbers lie between −4 and 4?

Number sequences

Copy and complete the following sequences and explain the rule.

1. 3, 8, 13, ☐, ☐, 28
2. 56, 54, 52, ☐, ☐
3. 3, 2, 1, ☐, ☐, ☐, −3
4. 92, 96, ☐, ☐, 108, 112
5. 830, 820, 810, ☐, ☐, ☐
6. 289, 294, 299, ☐, ☐, 314
7. −10, −8, −6, −4, ☐, ☐, ☐
8. 542, 538, 534, ☐, ☐
9. −12, −8, ☐, ☐, 4, 8

Rounding to the nearest 10

HELP BOX

47 rounded to the nearest 10 is 50 because it is nearer to 50 than to 40.

40   50

45 is also rounded to 50 even though it is exactly halfway between 40 and 50.

Round these numbers to the nearest 10.

1. 61   **4.** 85   **7.** 96

2. 34   **5.** 49   **8.** 65

3. 68   **6.** 16   **9.** 7

Rounding to the nearest 100

HELP BOX

628 rounded to the nearest 100 is 600 because it is closer to 600 than to 700.

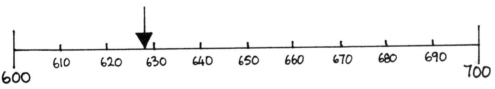

600   610   620   630   640   650   660   670   680   690   700

650 rounded to the nearest 100 is 700, even though it is exactly halfway between 600 and 700.

Round these numbers to the nearest 100 – you may like to use a number line to help.

1. 589   **4.** 349   **7.** 309

2. 123   **5.** 261   **8.** 150

3. 724   **6.** 485   **9.** 777

CHECK UP I

Write the number which is:

  I. 100 more than 567

  2. 10 less than 307

  3. 1 more than 599

  4. 100 less than 187

Copy and complete these number sequences.

  5. 31, 26, 21, ☐, ☐, 6

  6. 173, 176, 179, ☐, ☐

  7. Round 66 to the nearest 10.

  8. Write all the odd numbers between 96 and 108.

  9. Arrange these in order, the smallest first:
   £3·50, £3·15, £3·05, £3·55, £3·95.

10. Write all the numbers between −5 and 3.

II. Round 381 to the nearest hundred.

12. Arrange these in order, the largest first:
   110 cm, 1 m, 1·20 m, $1\frac{1}{2}$ m, 140 cm.

Doubles to 20 + 20

  I. 12 + 12 = ☐

  2. Double 9

  3. Half of 26

  4. 14 = ☐ + ☐

  5. 15 + 15 = ☐

  6. Double 19

  7. Half of 32

  8. ☐ + ☐ = 28

  9. 17 + 17 = ☐

10. Half of 16

II. 13 + 13 = ☐

12. Half of 22

Doubles and halves of multiples of 5

1. 35 + 35 = ☐

2. Double 75

3. Half of 100

4. 140 = ☐ + ☐

5. 95 + 95 = ☐

6. Half of 170

7. 55 + 55 = ☐

8. 180 = ☐ + ☐

9. Double 65

10. 90 + 90 = ☐

11. 50 = ☐ + ☐

12. Half of 90

Near doubles

HELP BOX

Use your knowledge of doubles to help with these.

For example, 25 + 26 = 51 because it is
1 more than double 25;

80 + 70 = 150 because it is two 80s minus 10,
or two 70s plus 10.

1. 16 + 15 = ☐

2. 45 + 46 = ☐

3. 19 + 18 = ☐

4. 31 + 30 = ☐

5. 27 + 25 = ☐

6. 50 + 60 = ☐

7. 75 + 74 = ☐

8. 17 + 16 = ☐

9. 35 + 36 = ☐

10. 14 + 13 = ☐

11. 65 + 67 = ☐

12. 90 + 80 = ☐

Counting on and counting back

HELP BOX

Work out these sums mentally by counting on or counting back. For example, 64 − 6 can be worked out by counting back three lots of 2 from 64 to leave 58.

Count back in twos.

1. 56 − 8 = ☐

2. 62 − 4 = ☐

3. 74 − 6 = ☐

Count on in fives.

4. 45 + 35 = ☐

5. 55 + 25 = ☐

6. 75 + 15 = ☐

Count on in tens.

7. 37 + 50 = ☐

8. 43 + 30 = ☐

9. 59 + 40 = ☐

Count back in tens.

10. 74 − 30 = ☐

11. 96 − 60 = ☐

12. 89 − 40 = ☐

Making 100

1. 45 + ☐ = 100

2. 21 + ☐ = 100

3. 89 + ☐ = 100

4. ☐ + 91 = 100

5. ☐ + 35 = 100

6. 74 + ☐ = 100

7. 66 + ☐ = 100

8. 28 + ☐ = 100

HELP BOX

You might like to use a number line to help find number pairs that make 100.

9. ☐ + 30 = 100

10. 51 + ☐ = 100

11. ☐ + 29 = 100

12. ☐ + 7 = 100

Making 1000 with multiples of 100

1. $700 + \square = 1000$
2. $100 + \square = 1000$
3. $500 + \square = 1000$
4. $\square + 200 = 1000$
5. $400 + \square = 1000$
6. $\square + 0 = 1000$

Number bonds to 20

1. $9 + 7 = \square$
2. $8 + \square = 13$
3. $17 - \square = 12$
4. $11 - 8 = \square$
5. $13 + \square = 19$
6. $8 + 6 = \square$
7. $9 + \square = 20$
8. $17 - 8 = \square$
9. $5 + \square = 14$
10. $12 - \square = 4$
11. $\square + 3 = 20$
12. $19 - \square = 8$
13. $7 + 6 = \square$
14. $13 - 8 = \square$
15. $20 - \square = 12$
16. $10 - \square = 4$

17. $\square - 9 = 11$
18. $8 + \square = 17$
19. $15 - \square = 9$
20. $\square - 6 = 11$

Finding the difference

HELP BOX

When two numbers are close together, count
up to find the difference between them.
For example, to find the difference between 303
and 297, count on 6 from 297 to make 303.

1. 72 – 69 = ☐
2. 502 take away 498
3. 101 minus 93
4. 805 – 792 = ☐
5. 81 – 76 = ☐
6. 901 subtract 890

7. What is the difference
   between 208 and 197?
8. 610 – 598 = ☐
9. 73 subtract 65
10. 403 – 392 = ☐
11. 702 take away 689
12. 106 – 99 = ☐

CHECK UP 2

1. 11 + ☐ = 20
2. Double 17
3. 600 + ☐ = 1000
4. What is the difference
   between 57p and 62p?
5. Half of 150
6. 703 – 698 = ☐
7. 18 + 19 = ☐

8. Double 85
9. 65 + 30 = ☐
10. ☐ + 47 = 100
11. 68 + 8 = ☐
12. 300 + ☐ = 1000

Adding and subtracting 11, 21, 31...

1. 34 + 21 = ☐
2. 56 + 31 = ☐
3. 48 + 41 = ☐
4. 79 + 21 = ☐
5. 83 + 11 = ☐
6. 65 + 31 = ☐

When adding 21, it is easier to add 20 and then add 1 more.

HELP BOX

When subtracting 21, subtract 20 and then take away 1 more.

7. 53 – 21 = ☐
8. 29 – 11 = ☐
9. 50 – 31 = ☐
10. 63 – 51 = ☐
11. 71 – 41 = ☐
12. 99 – 31 = ☐

Adding and subtracting 9, 19, 29...

1. 64 + 9 = ☐
2. 53 + 19 = ☐
3. 48 + 29 = ☐
4. 65 + 19 = ☐
5. 37 + 39 = ☐
6. 16 + 49 = ☐

When adding 19, it is easier to add 20 and then subtract 1.

HELP BOX

When subtracting 19, subtract 20 and then add 1.

7. 48 – 19 = ☐
8. 67 – 29 = ☐
9. 22 – 9 = ☐
10. 96 – 49 = ☐
11. 35 – 19 = ☐
12. 53 – 29 = ☐

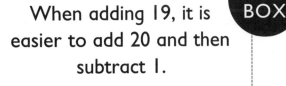
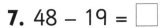

Adding more than two numbers

1. $8 + 4 + 2 = \square$

2. $9p + 15p + 5p = \square$

3. $9 + \square + 11 = 28$

4. $6 + 7 + 5 + 3 = \square$

5. $11 + 12 + \square = 32$

6. $17 \text{ cm} + 5 \text{ cm} + 12 \text{ cm} + 3 \text{ cm} = \square$

7. $8 + \square + 7 = 27$

8. $\square + 6 + 3 + 4 = 18$

9. $10p + 8p + 6p + 2p = \square$

10. $3 + 8 + 7 + \square = 19$

11. $12 + \square + 7 + 8 = 30$

12. $4 + 17 + 16 = \square$

HELP BOX

Try to find pairs of numbers that make 10 and add these first. If there are no pairs that make 10, find pairs that make 20.

Addition and subtraction patterns

Complete the missing totals.

1. $14 + \square = 19$

   $14 + 15 = \square$

   $14 + 25 = \square$

   $14 + \square = 49$

   $14 + 45 = \square$

   $14 + 85 = \square$

HELP BOX

Look at the pattern in these sums and use it to help work out the answer.

2. $76 - \square = 73$

   $76 - 13 = \square$

   $76 - 23 = \square$

   $76 - \square = 43$

   $76 - 43 = \square$

   $76 - \square = 13$

Adding and subtracting single digits

1. $672 + 5 = \square$
2. $849 - 7 = \square$
3. $235 + \square = 238$
4. $795 - \square = 791$
5. $600 - 7 = \square$
6. $\square + 7 = 368$
7. $\square - 8 = 491$
8. $409 - 6 = \square$
9. $377 - \square = 372$
10. $\square - 3 = 543$
11. $504 + \square = 508$
12. $\square - 2 = 621$

$672 + 5 =$

Adding to multiples of 100

1. $400 + 65 = \square$
2. $700 + \square = 721$
3. $\square + 91 = 891$
4. $300 + 52 = \square$
5. $200 + \square = 218$
6. $\square + 39 = 139$
7. $500 + 55 = \square$
8. $600 + \square = 640$
9. $\square + 14 = 414$
10. $900 + 92 = \square$
11. $700 + \square = 743$
12. $\square + 81 = 881$

Subtracting a single digit

1. $500 - 6 = \boxed{}$
2. $800 - 2 = \boxed{}$
3. $600 - \boxed{} = 595$
4. $\boxed{} - 3 = 397$
5. $\boxed{} - 8 = 192$
6. $700 - \boxed{} = 691$
7. $900 - 4 = \boxed{}$
8. $400 - \boxed{} = 398$
9. $\boxed{} - 5 = 295$
10. $600 - \boxed{} = 599$
11. $500 - 7 = \boxed{}$
12. $200 - 8 = \boxed{}$

Adding to multiples of 10

1. $30 + 27 = \boxed{}$
2. $80 + 14 = \boxed{}$
3. $60 + \boxed{} = 95$
4. $50 + \boxed{} = 89$
5. $20 + 56 = \boxed{}$
6. $\boxed{} + 23 = 73$
7. $\boxed{} + 51 = 81$
8. $40 + 32 = \boxed{}$
9. $\boxed{} + 28 = 88$
10. $70 + \boxed{} = 95$
11. $30 + 22 = \boxed{}$
12. $\boxed{} + 31 = 61$

Subtracting from multiples of 100

1. 700 – 5 = ☐
2. 900 – 8 = ☐
3. 400 – 6 = ☐
4. 200 – ☐ = 193
5. ☐ – 2 = 298
6. 800 – ☐ = 791
7. ☐ – 4 = 596
8. 200 – 9 = ☐
9. 300 – ☐ = 292
10. 600 – 7 = ☐
11. 500 – 1 = ☐
12. ☐ – 7 = 893

Adding two digits to multiples of 10

1. 60 + 38 = ☐
2. ☐ + 43 = 63
3. 30 + ☐ = 78
4. 50 + 32 = ☐
5. ☐ + 71 = 91
6. 60 + ☐ = 85
7. 50 + 39 = ☐
8. ☐ + 66 = 96
9. 70 + ☐ = 82
10. 40 + 41 = ☐
11. ☐ + 27 = 57
12. 30 + ☐ = 89

CHECK UP 3

1. 500 – 7 = ☐
2. 40 + 37 = ☐
3. 54 + 29 = ☐
4. 200 + ☐ = 209
5. 15p + 9p + 11p + 7p = ☐
6. 789 – ☐ = 782
7. 72 – 31 = ☐
8. ☐ + 61 = 91
9. 83 – 39 = ☐
10. 12 cm + 9 cm + 8 cm = ☐
11. 45 + 19 = ☐
12. **Copy and complete the missing totals:**

   69 – 5 = ☐   69 – ☐ = 44   69 – ☐ = 14

   69 – 15 = ☐   69 – 35 = ☐

Adding and subtracting pairs of two-digit numbers

1. 32 + 24 = ☐
2. 45 + 21 = ☐
3. 56 – 25 = ☐
4. 79 – 45 = ☐
5. ☐ + 67 = 88
6. ☐ + 23 = 76

7. 84 – ☐ = 51
8. 69 – ☐ = 22
9. ☐ – 35 = 33
10. ☐ – 61 = 27
11. 57 + ☐ = 98
12. 43 + ☐ = 75

Adding and subtracting multiples of 10

HELP BOX

Try these in two steps so you get to 100 first.
For example, to add 80 and 60, count on 20 from 80 to
get to 100, then count on another 4 tens to 140.
130 – 70 count back 3 tens to 100 then another 4 tens to 60.

1. 70 + 50 = ☐
2. 90 + 40 = ☐
3. 140 – 50 = ☐
4. 80 + ☐ = 130
5. 170 – ☐ = 90
6. ☐ – 70 = 60

7. 150 – 80 = ☐
8. 90 + ☐ = 150
9. 140 – ☐ = 60
10. ☐ – 30 = 80
11. 120 – 70 = ☐
12. 80 + 40 = ☐

Making the next 100

**Work out what needs to be added to these three-digit
multiples of 10 to make the next highest multiple of 100.**

1. 370 + ☐ = 400
2. 520 + ☐ = 600
3. 290 + ☐ = 300
4. 860 + ☐ = 900
5. 550 + ☐ = 600
6. 130 + ☐ = 200

7. 480 + ☐ = 500
8. 610 + ☐ = 700
9. 740 + ☐ = 800
10. 220 + ☐ = 300
11. 560 + ☐ = 600
12. 180 + ☐ = 200

More adding and subtracting multiples of 10

Count on or back in tens to help with these.

HELP BOX

1. 123 − 40 = ☐
2. 57 + 70 = ☐
3. 89 + ☐ = 129
4. 157 − ☐ = 97
5. ☐ + 50 = 116
6. ☐ − 30 = 94

7. 61 + 70 = ☐
8. 118 − 40 = ☐
9. 64 + 80 = ☐
10. ☐ + 50 = 147
11. 136 − ☐ = 86
12. ☐ − 90 = 55

Adding and subtracting multiples of 100

HELP BOX

Try these in two steps, make 1000 first by counting on or back in hundreds. For example, to make 800 + 500 count on 200 to make 1000 then another 300 to make 1300.

1. 600 + 500 = ☐
2. 900 + ☐ = 1300
3. 1500 − 700 = ☐
4. 1400 − ☐ = 600
5. ☐ + 300 = 1100
6. 1200 − ☐ = 400

7. 1600 − 700 = ☐
8. ☐ + 500 = 1400
9. 900 + 700 = ☐
10. 1300 − ☐ = 500
11. ☐ − 900 = 200
12. 700 + 600 = ☐

Adding and subtracting 10 or 100

1. 452 + 100 = ☐
2. 197 − 10 = ☐
3. 712 − 100 = ☐
4. 309 + 10 = ☐
5. 903 − 10 = ☐
6. ☐ − 100 = 512
7. 201 − ☐ = 101
8. ☐ − 10 = 98
9. 764 + 100 = ☐
10. 892 + 10 = ☐
11. 511 − 10 = ☐
12. 785 + ☐ = 795

Subtracting from 'teens' numbers

1. 15 − 8 = ☐
2. 13 subtract 6
3. Take 7 away from 15
4. 16 − ☐ = 9
5. ☐ − 8 = 8
6. 15 minus 9
7. ☐ − 7 = 6
8. 6 less than 15
9. 13 subtract 9
10. 14 − 6 = ☐
11. 13 − ☐ = 8
12. 14 take away 8

HELP BOX

Do these in two steps, crossing ten as the middle stage. For example,
13 − 8 = 13 − 3 − 5 =
10 − 5 = 5.

More adding and
subtracting single digits

HELP BOX

Work these out in two steps by crossing a multiple of 10 first.
For example, 76 + 7 = 76 + 4 + 3 = 80 + 3 = 83;
63 − 6 = 63 − 3 − 3 = 60 − 3 = 57.

I. 26 + 8 = ☐

2. 47 − 8 = ☐

3. 34 + 7 = ☐

4. 75 − 8 = ☐

5. 68 + ☐ = 73

6. 52 − ☐ = 48

7. 29 + ☐ = 34

8. 91 − ☐ = 88

9. ☐ − 5 = 38

10. ☐ + 6 = 91

11. ☐ − 7 = 44

12. ☐ + 8 = 23

More finding the difference

HELP BOX

Remember to count on from the smaller
number. For example, to find the difference between 1005 and
998 count on 2 from 998 to make 1000 then count on another
5 to make 7.

I. 1004 − 996 = ☐

2. 998 + ☐ = 1003

3. 1003 − 990 = ☐

4. 992 + ☐ = 1001

5. 1010 − 999 = ☐

6. 995 + ☐ = 1008

7. 1006 − 998 = ☐

8. 997 + ☐ = 1004

9. 1005 − 994 = ☐

10. 999 + ☐ = 1015

11. 1001 − 993 = ☐

12. 995 + ☐ = 1002

Adding and subtracting any two-digit numbers

Try working these out mentally and discuss the way you did them with a friend. Did you use the same methods?

1. 27 + 35 = ☐
2. 32 + 49 = ☐
3. 51 − 28 = ☐
4. 47 − 38 = ☐
5. ☐ + 22 = 61
6. ☐ − 53 = 21

7. 42 − ☐ = 14
8. 35 + 37 = ☐
9. 97 − 28 = ☐
10. 58 + ☐ = 91
11. 49 + 31 = ☐
12. 73 − 25 = ☐

CHECK UP 4

1. 620 + ☐ = 700
2. 800 + 300 = ☐
3. 16 subtract 7
4. ☐ − 7 = 25
5. 32 plus 43
6. 130 − ☐ = 70
7. 997 + ☐ = 1005
8. 602 subtract 10
9. ☐ + 40 = 400
10. 56 + 28 = ☐
11. 71 − ☐ = 65
12. 992 + ☐ = 1006

Multiplication and division facts – 2 times table

1. 2 x 6 = ☐
2. Multiply 3 by 2
3. How many 2s in 16?
4. 2 x 0 = ☐
5. Divide 20 by 2
6. 14 ÷ 2 = ☐
7. 2 x ☐ = 2
8. Five twos
9. 2 x 9 = ☐
10. 2 x ☐ = 8
11. Divide 4 by 2
12. How many 2s in 18?

Multiplication and division facts – 5 times table

1. 5 x 4 = ☐
2. 30 ÷ 5 = ☐
3. How many 5s in 40?
4. 6 multiplied by 5
5. 5 x ☐ = 15
6. Ten fives
7. 5 x 0 = ☐
8. 45 ÷ 5 = ☐
9. Divide 35 by 5
10. 5 x ☐ = 10
11. How many 5s in 20?

Multiplication and division facts – 10 times table

1. 80 ÷ 10 = ☐
2. Six tens
3. 10 x 3 = ☐
4. 10 x 0 = ☐
5. How many 10s in 50?
6. Divide 20 by 10
7. 90 ÷ 10 = ☐
8. 8 multiplied by 10
9. 10 ÷ 1 = ☐
10. Four tens
11. 10 x 5 = ☐
12. 70 divided by 10

Multiples

What is the multiple of:

1. 10 before 80?
2. 5 after 35?
3. 2 after 28?
4. 100 before 700?
5. 5 before 160?
6. 2 before 50?
7. 100 after 900?
8. 10 after 190?

HELP BOX

2, 4, 6, 8 are all multiples of 2, as 2 will divide exactly into each of them.

9. Which of these are multiples of 5? 34, 52, 25, 35, 51
10. Which of these are multiples of 2? 68, 83, 61, 56, 80
11. What are the first five multiples of 10?
12. All multiples of 5 end in 0 or 5, true or false?

Multiplication and division facts – 3 times table

1. 3 x 4 = ☐
2. 18 ÷ 3 = ☐
3. 3 x ☐ = 21
4. 30 ÷ 3 = ☐
5. 3 x 0 = ☐
6. 3 x 9 = ☐
7. 15 ÷ 3 = ☐
8. 6 ÷ 3 = ☐
9. 3 x 8 = ☐
10. 3 ÷ 3 = ☐
11. 3 x 10 = ☐
12. 3 x ☐ = 18

Multiplication and division facts – 4 times table

1. 4 x 5 = ☐
2. 12 ÷ 4 = ☐
3. 4 x 8 = ☐
4. ☐ ÷ 4 = 4
5. 4 x ☐ = 4
6. 4 x 10 = ☐
7. 4 x 0 = ☐
8. 4 x ☐ = 36
9. 24 ÷ 4 = ☐
10. 8 ÷ ☐ = 2
11. 32 ÷ 4 = ☐
12. 4 x 7 = ☐

Halving odd numbers

HELP
BOX

1. $13 \div 2 = \Box$
2. $\frac{1}{2}$ of 21
3. $\Box \div 2 = 5\frac{1}{2}$

Half of 5 is $2\frac{1}{2}$

4. Half of 45
5. $29 \div 2 = \Box$
6. Double $9\frac{1}{2}$
7. $17 \div 2 = \Box$
8. $12\frac{1}{2} \times 2 = \Box$
9. $9 \div 2 = \Box$
10. Half of 13
11. Double $13\frac{1}{2}$
12. Half of 23

Mixed doubles and halves

1. $45 \times 2 = \Box$
2. $\Box \times 2 = 32$
3. $160 \div 2 = \Box$
4. Half of 19
5. Twice 75
6. $\frac{1}{2}$ of 400
7. $10\frac{1}{2} \times 2$
8. Double 18
9. Twice 100
10. $14 \times 2 = \Box$
11. Half of 70
12. $26 \div 2 = \Box$

CHECK UP 5

1. 5 multiplied by 3
2. How many twos in 18?
3. Half of 13
4. What are the first three multiples of 10?
5. 3 x ☐ = 12
6. Divide 35 by 5
7. Double $9\frac{1}{2}$

8. What is the next multiple of 2 after 14?
9. Eight tens
10. ☐ ÷ 4 = 1
11. $\frac{1}{2}$ of 110
12. 5 x 9 = ☐
13. Twice 80
14. 30 ÷ 3 = ☐

Finding quarters

HELP BOX

To find quarters you can work out half of one half.
For example, one quarter of 24 is 6 because half of 24
is 12 and half of 12 is 6.

Find a quarter of these numbers.

1. 20
2. 100
3. 32
4. 160
5. 600
6. 12

7. 14
8. 36
9. 200
10. 10
11. 28
12. 40

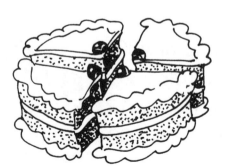

Related facts

HELP
BOX

If you know that 4 x 7 = 28 you also know that:
7 x 4 = 28,   28 ÷ 4 = 7 and 28 ÷ 7 = 4.

Write 3 other multiplication or division facts about each of these sums.

1. 45 ÷ 5 = 9   **3.** 8 x 6 = 48
2. 3 x 8 = 24   **4.** 28 ÷ 7 = 4

Use each set of numbers to write 4 different multiplication or division facts.

5. 3, 5, 15   **8.** 21, 7, 3
6. 14, 2, 7   **9.** 18, 9, 2
7. 10, 80, 8   **10.** 5, 35, 7

Multiplying by 1, 10 or 100

1. 7 x 10 = ☐
2. 4 x 100 = ☐
3. ☐ x 100 = 200
4. ☐ x 10 = 50
5. 9 x 1 = ☐
6. 8 x 10 = ☐
7. ☐ x 100 = 900
8. 6 x 1 = ☐
9. ☐ x 10 = 70
10. 5 x 100 = ☐
11. 1 x 1 = ☐
12. 3 x 100 = ☐

Dividing by 100 or by 10

1. $600 \div 100 = \square$
2. $400 \div 10 = \square$
3. $\frac{1}{100}$ of 900
4. $300 \div \square = 30$
5. Divide 500 by 100
6. How many tens in 200?
7. $\square \div 100 = 4$
8. $700 \div 10 = \square$
9. $\frac{1}{10}$ of 800
10. $\square \div 10 = 60$
11. $\square \div 100 = 1$
12. $800 \div \square = 8$

Multiplying multiples of 10

1. $60 \times 3 = \square$
2. $50 \times \square = 250$
3. $\square \times 2 = 140$
4. $40 \times 4 = \square$
5. $\square \times 10 = 600$
6. $80 \times 3 = \square$
7. $90 = 30 \times \square$
8. $400 = \square \times 5$
9. $90 \times 2 = \square$
10. $60 \times 4 = \square$
11. $\square \times 3 = 210$
12. $80 \times \square = 320$

Multiplying two-digit numbers by 2, 3, 4 and 5

1. 21 x 3 = ☐

2. 42 x 2 = ☐

3. ☐ x 5 = 55

4. 32 x ☐ = 96

5. ☐ x 4 = 88

6. 33 x 2 = ☐

7. ☐ x 3 = 69

8. 21 x 4 = ☐

9. 12 x ☐ = 48

10. ☐ x 3 = 99

11. 11 x ☐ = 44

12. 21 x ☐ = 63

Multiplying and adding

1. 64 = ☐ x 3 + 4

2. 21 x 4 + 6 = ☐

3. 12 x 3 + ☐ = 41

4. 70 x 4 − 8 = ☐

5. 87 = ☐ x 2 + 7

6. 100 = 32 x ☐ + 4

7. 24 x 2 + 7 = ☐

8. 64 = ☐ x 5 + 9

9. 51 = 22 x 2 + ☐

10. 125 = ☐ x 3 + 5

11. 172 = ☐ x 2 + 12

12. 33 x 3 + 5 = ☐

CHECK UP 6

1. $70 \times \boxed{} = 350$
2. Quarter of 24
3. Write 4 different multiplication and division facts about these numbers: 3, 4, 12.
4. $32 \times 3 = \boxed{}$
5. $\frac{1}{10}$ of 900
6. $700 \div \boxed{} = 70$
7. $69 = 21 \times 3 + \boxed{}$
8. $\boxed{} \times 100 = 400$
9. $25 \times \boxed{} + 19 = 69$
10. Quarter of 100
11. $300 \div \boxed{} = 3$
12. $12 \times \boxed{} = 48$

Money

Find the total of these amounts.

1. £5·20 and £1·30
2. £1·75 and 25p
3. £4·10 and £2·50
4. £1·99 and 57p

How much change would you get from £5 if you spent:

5. £1·50?
6. £3·99?
7. £4·85?
8. 75p?
9. Which 5 coins would make 75p?
10. How many 10ps in £3?
11. Pens cost 80p. How much would 5 pens cost?
12. How many 50ps in £5·50?

Time

How many:

1. days in 3 weeks?
2. minutes in 4 hours?
3. months in 2 years?

How many minutes between:

4. 1:20 and 1:55?
5. 11:15 and 12?
6. 6:30 and quarter past 7?

Write the time 45 minutes after:

7. `2:10`

8. `6:40`

9.

Measures

How many:

1. metres in 2 kilometres?
2. grams in half a kilogram?
3. millimetres in 10 centimetres?
4. millilitres in $6\frac{1}{2}$ litres?
5. A biscuit weighs 25 g. What would 4 biscuits weigh?
6. Three ribbons measuring 35 cm, 45 cm and half a metre are joined together. What is the total length?
7. How many 50 millilitre cups can be filled from a 1 litre bottle?
8. What is the total weight of all 3 parcels?

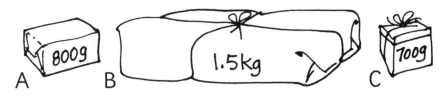

9. What is the difference in weight between A and C?

CHECK UP 7

1. What time will each of these clocks show after 15 minutes?

2. How much change would you get from £10 if you spent £8·99?

3. Write a weight between 1 kg and 2 kg.

4. How many days in 10 weeks?

5. What is the difference between £1·99 and £2·05?

6. Arrange these snakes in order, the shortest first.

    A 75 cm   B 1·25 m   C 98 cm   D $\frac{1}{2}$ m

7. What is the difference in length between the longest and shortest snake?

8. Snake C is 37 cm shorter than snake B, true or false?

9. A film starts at 6:15 and lasts for $1\frac{1}{2}$ hours. What time does it end?

10. Which 3 coins make £1·70?